WORDS THEIR WAY®

WORD STUDY IN ACTION • DERIVATIONAL RELATIONS

Glenview, Illinois

Boston, Massachusetts

Chandler, Arizona

Upper Saddle River, New Jersey

ALWAYS LEARNING

PEARSON

ISBN-13: 978-1-4284-3135-5
ISBN-10:   1-4284-3135-7
        18   17

Contents

Prefixes pre-, fore-, post-, after-

pre-	fore-	post-	after-
prewar	forethought	postwar	afterthought
afterword	foreword	preseason	forearm
postscript	afternoon	predate	preoccupied
postseason	prejudge	preposition	postdate
forecourt	predetermine	foresight	prefix
foreknowledge	forewarn	aftertaste	forego

Sort 1: Prefixes pre-, fore-, post-, after-

1

Prefixes pre-, fore-, post-, after-

pre-	fore-	post-	after-
prewar	forethought	postwar	afterthought

1. Write the definition of each prefix.
2. Write a word containing that prefix and its meaning.
3. Draw a picture to illustrate the word you defined.

pre-: _____

Word: _____

Definition: _____

fore-: _____

Word: _____

Definition: _____

post-: _____

Word: _____

Definition: _____

after-: _____

Word: _____

Definition: _____

fondness	graceful	restless
beautiful	skillfulness	politeness
truthful	priceless	friendliness
fanciful	flawless	emptiness
careful	tireless	respectful
speechless	darkness	grateful
kindness	worthless	breathless
flawlessness	delightful	thoughtlessness

Review Suffixes -ness, -ful, -less

-ness	-ful	-less	Combination of Suffixes
neatness	**useful**	**useless**	**usefulness**

1. Read each sentence. Choose one word from the box that best completes the sentence. (Note: Not all words have to be used and each word can be used only once.)

2. Add the suffix -ness, -ful, -less, or a combination of these suffixes to the word and write it on the line. (Change -y to i as necessary.)

thought	worth	breath	grace	flaw	fancy	kind	skill
delight	friend	respect	dark	fond	speech	polite	care
beauty	price	rest	tire	truth	grateful	empty	neat

1. The stitching on the designer gown was _____.

2. You have to be _____ when walking on ice.

3. Michael was too _____ to sleep.

4. The fake money was completely _____.

5. The flowers in the meadow were very _____.

6. We were _____ when the principal visited our class.

7. Without a flashlight it is hard to walk in _____.

8. The dog showed its _____ by wagging its tail.

9. She is so _____ that she never trips or falls.

10. I was impressed by his _____ when he remembered my birthday.

11. I became _____ while running to the bus.

12. Listening to the holiday concert was _____.

confess	election	correct
possession	collect	depression
discuss	correction	impress
confession	instruct	process
selection	discussion	select
collection	instruction	procession
protect	inspect	protection
possess	inspection	elect
depress	impression	

-ss + -ion	Base -ss	-ct + -ion	Base -ct
expression	**express**	**subtraction**	**subtract**

Read each sentence. Choose one word from the pair in parentheses that best completes the sentence and write it on the line. Place an n above the nouns and a v above the verbs.

1. We scheduled an _____ for our car. (inspect/inspection)

2. That rare baseball card is my _____. (possess/possession)

3. The fifth graders will vote to _____ a new class president. (elect/election)

4. I have 150 marbles in my _____. (collect/collection)

5. A mother bear will always try to _____ her cubs. (protect/protection)

6. At the end of the day, the bank tellers _____ the checks. (process/procession)

7. We had a _____ about ways to help people in our community. (discuss/discussion)

8. With so many delicious foods, it's hard to _____ my favorite! (select/selection)

9. The _____ on his face was one of pure joy. (express/expression)

10. This summer my father will _____ the swim team at our town pool. (instruct/instruction)

11. The seashell left a perfect _____ in the sand. (impress/impression)

12. Our teacher asked the class to _____ who left the gift on her desk. (confess/confession)

Adding -ion and -ian (With No Spelling Change)

electric	musician	interrupt
suggestion	optician	invention
clinician	adoption	digest
suggest	optic	invent
interruption	adopt	electrician

digestion
exhaust
clinic
music
exhaustion

Adding -ion and -ian (With No Spelling Change)

-ic + -ian **magician**	Base -ic **magic**	-t + -ion **prevention**	Base -t **prevent**

1. Read each sentence.
2. Complete each sentence by adding the ending -ion or -ian to the word in parentheses and write the word on the line. Before adding the ending, think about if the word refers to a person who does something.

1. When the power went out we had to call an _____.
   (electric)

2. She practiced her violin every day to become a better
   _____. (music)

3. The _____ studied only certain diseases. (clinic)

4. Pardon the _____, but I need an answer now. (interrupt)

5. The _____ entertained the children at the party.
   (magic)

6. The scientist's new _____ was a robot that can clean
   floors. (invent)

7. Sitting still can help the _____ of whatever you just
   ate. (digest)

8. My _____ checks my eyesight twice a year. (optic)

9. We liked her _____ so much that we followed it
   immediately. (suggest)

10. We had to put my cat's kittens up for _____. (adopt)

11. After the race, all the runners showed their _____.
    (exhaust)

12. As part of fire _____ week, we practiced exiting the
    school quickly. (prevent)

reproduce	creation	calculate
introduction	hibernation	fascinate
coordination	reduction	concentration
generation	decorate	reproduction
imitation	coordinate	reduce
imitate	concentrate	create
calculation	generate	hibernate
decoration	fascination	introduce

Adding -ion (With e-Drop and Spelling Change)

e-Drop + -tion	Base -ce	e-Drop + -ion	Base -te
production	**produce**	**location**	**locate**

Make new words by adding -ion to the following base words. (Drop e and make spelling changes as necessary.) Then write a definition of the new word.

1. create _____ Definition: _____

2. introduce _____ Definition: _____

3. coordinate _____ Definition: _____

4. reduce _____ Definition: _____

5. fascinate _____ Definition: _____

6. decorate _____ Definition: _____

7. imitate _____ Definition: _____

8. generate _____ Definition: _____

9. reproduce _____ Definition: _____

10. hibernate _____ Definition: _____

11. concentrate _____ Definition: _____

12. calculate _____ Definition: _____

Sort 5: Adding -ion (With e-Drop and Spelling Change)

persuade	decision	emit
omission	division	permission
intrude	invade	transmission
collide	invasion	omit
submission	divide	conclusion
erode	intrusion	transmit
erosion	persuasion	emission
decide	collision	submit
permit	conclude	

Adding -ion (With Predictable Changes in Consonants)

-it > -ission	Base -it	-de > -sion	Base -de
admission	admit	explosion	explode

1. Read each sentence. Choose a base word from the box that best completes the sentence. (Note: Not all words have to be used and each word can be used only once.)

2. Add -ion to the word. (Drop -de and -it and add -sion and -ission as necessary.) Write the word on the line.

persuade	transmit	emit	permit	admit
conclude	erode	collide	invade	explode
divide	omit	submit	decide	intrude

1. The _____ damaged both cars.

2. By using _____, Randy convinced his mother to let him go out.

3. _____ is wearing away the banks of the river.

4. We decided upon equal _____ of cookies between students.

5. Emma asked the teacher for _____ to leave class.

6. _____ of information via the Internet is becoming more common.

7. He was angry at the _____ of his name from the program.

8. The _____ of light from streetlights can make it hard to see stars.

9. The army fought but could not stop their enemy's _____.

10. I read the _____ to see how the book would end.

11. My parents paid for my _____ to the movies.

12. Jamal worked hard on his poetry _____ for the contest.

Consonant Alternation: Silent and Sounded

moist	limb	bombard	haste
muscle	crumb	resignation	limber
columnist	column	soften	designate
hasten	soft	crumble	resign
bomb	moisten	design	muscular

Silent Consonant	Sounded Consonant
sign	**signal**

1. Read the words in the box.
2. Write each word in the column that shows whether it has a silent or sounded consonant.
3. Underline the consonants that alternate between silent and sounded.

bomb	moist	crumb	design	muscle
resignation	designate	muscular	limb	moisten
crumble	limber	hasten	haste	soften
bombard	columnist	soft	column	resign

Silent Consonant	Sounded Consonant

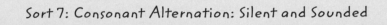

Vowel Alternation: Long to Short

breath	revise	athlete	mine
natural	criminal	revision	breathe
athletic	mineral	crime	nation
nature	national	ignite	grateful
ignition	gratitude	precision	precise

Long Vowel	Short Vowel
type	**typical**

1. Read each sentence.
2. Choose one word from the pair in parentheses that best completes the sentence and write it on the line.
3. Place a long vowel symbol (ˉ) over the long vowels. Place a short vowel symbol (˘) over the short vowels.

1. Esteban had few errors to _____ on his written report. (revise/revision)

2. High in the mountains it is harder to _____. (breath/breathe)

3. Taylor is so _____ that she can run a mile in 6 minutes. (athlete/athletic)

4. Andy showed his _____ for the present by writing a thank-you note. (grateful/gratitude)

5. I left _____ directions so Sue would know where to find us. (precise/precision)

6. They dig up gold and silver in this _____. (mine/mineral)

7. Turning the key in the _____ will start the car. (ignite/ignition)

8. Breaking into someone's house is a _____. (crime/criminal)

9. The company delivers its product to people all across the _____. (nation/national)

10. The _____ home for a bear is the woods. (nature/natural)

compete	rite	reptilian	relative
natural	define	definition	mineral
flame	flammable	competition	reside
confide	confidence	reptile	mine
nature	relate	ritual	residence
major	majority		

Vowel Alternation: Long to Short or /ə/

Derived Word /ə/	Base Word Long Vowel	Derived Word Short Vowel	Base Word Long Vowel
composition	compose	cavity	cave

1. Read each sentence.
2. Choose one word from the box that best completes the sentence and write it on the line. (Note: Not all words have to be used and each word can be used only once.)
3. Place a short vowel symbol (˘) over the short vowels. Circle the vowels with the schwa sound.

flammable	compose	reptile	definition	compete	composition	relate
mine	rite	relative	reptilian	confidence	nature	cave
ritual	majority	competition	major	reside	confide	
residence	mineral	natural	flame	cavity	define	

1. Can you _____ this word for me?

2. The _____ of marriage is an important ceremony.

3. We were determined to win the _____.

4. The coach showed her _____ in Gabrielle by asking her to lead the warm-up.

5. The _____ of the class attended the baseball playoffs.

6. Do you _____ in this city?

7. The pianist also likes to _____ his own music.

8. We explored the underground _____.

9. Javier admired the color of the _____.

10. The couple prefers a _____ setting for their wedding.

11. A snake is a kind of _____.

12. Gasoline is a _____ substance.

familiar	inspire	familiarity
combine	translate	perspire
preparation	combination	mobile
oppose	mobility	opposition
translation	perspiration	metallic
inspiration	prepare	metal

Base Word	Derived Word
similar	**similarity**

1. Complete each sentence by adding a new ending to the word in parentheses.
2. Write the derived word on the line.
3. Underline the stressed syllable in each derived word.

1. We showed our _____ to the plan by voting "no."
   (oppose)

2. Thanks to hours of _____, the party was a success.
   (prepare)

3. Valerie read the _____ of the French poem. (translate)

4. The _____ of peanut butter and jelly is delicious.
   (combine)

5. The shape of a bird wing was the _____ behind the new
   plane design. (inspire)

6. The old pipes gave the water a _____ taste. (metal)

7. Julie demonstrated a great _____ with where all the
   tools were kept. (familiar)

8. It was so hot outside that we were soon soaked with
   _____. (perspire)

9. Oiling its wheels increased the cart's _____. (mobile)

10. There's a _____ between my best friend's handwriting
    and mine. (similar)

Adding the Suffix -ity: Vowel Alternation (/ə/ to Short)

general	individuality	neutral	individual
generality	fatality	original	brutal
neutrality	formal	personality	normal
normality	personal	originality	brutality
formality	fatal	mentality	mental
national	inequal	nationality	inequality

/ə/	Accented
moral	**morality**

1. Read the paragraph below.
2. Find seven words with the schwa sound and write them on the lines in the first column.
3. Add the suffix -ity to each word and write the new word on the line next to it.
4. Reread all the words and choose one to use in a sentence.

Jess and Tim went to the general meeting for the art contest. They learned that they had to create original pieces and bring them to the library on National Street in two weeks. They decided to make individual pieces rather than work as a team. Both Jess and Tim created artwork that was very personal to them. Jess used neutral colors and painted one of her best paintings ever. Tim used clay to make an outstanding sculpture. At the formal awards ceremony, both Jess and Tim won prizes for their hard work!

/ə/ Words   **+ -ity**

1. _____   _____

2. _____   _____

3. _____   _____

4. _____   _____

5. _____   _____

6. _____   _____

7. _____   _____

Sentence: _____

_____

_____

Sort 11: Adding the Suffix -ity: Vowel Alternation (/ə/ to Short)

Base -m or -n	-ation	Base -e	-ption
exclaim	exclamation	assume	assumption
proclamation	acclaim	acclamation	consumption
presume	explain	presumption	proclaim
consume	resumption	explanation	conception
reclamation	conceive	reception	resume
reclaim	receive		

Adding Suffixes: Vowel Alternation (With Spelling Change)

Base -m or -n	-ation	Base -e	-ption
exclaim	**exclamation**	**assume**	**assumption**

Complete each sentence by adding the suffix -tion to the word in parentheses. (Change the spelling of the base word as necessary.) Write the word on the line.

1. My brother's _____ of vegetables is so large that we have to buy carrots every day. (consume)

2. Paul's _____ of the plan was great, but he did not follow through. (conceive)

3. The king's messenger read a _____ that ended the war. (proclaim)

4. Her _____ helped us understand how to play the game. (explain)

5. The winning team's _____ was heard as soon as the game ended. (exclaim)

6. The _____ of the game began after the rain stopped. (resume)

7. It is a _____ to think you are allowed to enter a home just because a door has been left open. (presume)

8. The _____ of the flooded land began when they pumped out the extra water. (reclaim)

9. Families and school faculty had a _____ to honor students' achievements. (receive)

10. Making an _____ about someone you don't know very well isn't fair. (assume)

verification	identification	notification
clarify	clarification	purify
verify	identify	magnify
qualify	notify	justify
clarify	clarification	purify
purification	magnification	unify
qualification	unification	multiply
multiplication		

Base -ify/-iply	Derived -ation
classify	classification

1. Read each sentence.
2. Choose one word from the pair in parentheses that best completes the sentence and write it on the line.
3. Place an n above the nouns and a v above the verbs.

1. The campers had to _____ the river water before they could drink it. (purify/purification)

2. We received a _____ in the mail that we were prizewinners. (notify/notification)

3. Amy needed further _____ before she understood what to do next. (clarify/clarification)

4. The family decided to _____ their lives by giving away their television. (simplify/simplification)

5. Can you _____ that this is the correct address? (verify/verification)

6. Malcolm had to show his _____ before he could board the airplane. (identify/identification)

7. The _____ was so strong we could see every hair on the beetle's legs. (magnify/magnification)

8. Rosa had a good excuse to _____ her action. (justify/justification)

9. Akina hoped she would _____ for the track finals. (qualify/qualification)

10. The coach hoped to _____ the team's thinking before the first game. (unify/unification)

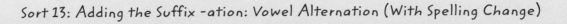

diplomat	defame	trivial
punish	diplomacy	diverse
academy	defamatory	diplomatic
syllable	pugnacious	triviality
diversion	copious	divert
academic	punitive	syllabic
impugn	pugnacity	allege
impunity	allegation	copy

1. Look at the word in each box.
2. Write one alternation of the word.
3. Then write a sentence or draw a picture that shows the meaning of the original word.

trivial

Alternation: _____

academy

Alternation: _____

copy

Alternation: _____

divert

Alternation: _____

mono-	bi-	tri-
monolingual	**bilingual**	**triangle**
biceps	monologue	biennial
monopod	tripod	tricolor
bisect	triennial	monopoly
trilogy	monorail	binary
monotone	trigonometry	bicameral
biweekly	tricentennial	monotony
triathlon	bimonthly	triplets

mono- **monolingual**	bi- **bilingual**	tri- **triangle**

1. Choose two prefixes (mono-, bi-, or tri-), and write one in the center of each web. Write the meaning below each prefix.
2. Fill in the surrounding ovals with words that begin with that prefix.
3. Write the meaning below each word.

Sort 15: Greek and Latin Prefixes mono-, bi-, tri-

Greek and Latin Prefixes inter-, sub-, over-

Internet	subtotal	overflow
overtake	interchange	interact
overwhelm	overthrow	intersect
subway	submerge	subfloor
subdivide	sublet	subtitle
overeager	overreact	suburban
intermediate	overstep	oversee

international
subhead
interconnect
interfere
overlook
intercept
overripe

inter-	sub-	over-
intermural	**subconscious**	**overrate**

1. Choose two prefixes (inter-, sub-, or over-), and write one in the center of each web. Write the meaning below each prefix. (Remember that sub- and over- have more than one meaning.)
2. Fill in the surrounding ovals with words that begin with that prefix.
3. Write the meaning below each word.

Sort 16: Greek and Latin Prefixes inter-, sub-, over-

quadr-	tetra-	quint-	pent-	dec-
quadruple	**tetrad**	**quintuple**	**pentagon**	**decimal**
tetralogy	tetrarchy	quintuplets	pentangle	quadrant
quadrangle	quadruplets	pentathlon	quintessence	decathlete
decimate	tetrapod	pentathlete	quintessential	quadruped
pentarchy	quadrennial	decathlon	pentad	

Sort 17: Number Prefixes quadr-, tetra-, quint-, pent-, dec-

quadr- **quadruple**	tetra- **tetrad**

quint- **quintuple**	pent- **pentagon**	dec- **decimal**

1. Choose four prefixes (quadr-, tetra-, quint-, pent-, or dec-) and write one in each box.

2. Write a sentence and draw a picture to illustrate the meaning of each prefix.

Prefix: _____

Sentence: _____

Prefix: _____

Sentence: _____

Prefix: _____

Sentence: _____

Prefix: _____

Sentence: _____

Sort 17: Number Prefixes quadr-, tetra-, quint-, pent-, dec-

inspection	support	portable
perspective	deport	speculate
import	spectator	transport
report	prospect	portfolio
inspector	heliport	spectacle
spectacular	spectrum	opportunity

spect	port
respect	**export**

1. Read the word root in the center of each web and write the meaning below it.
2. Fill in the surrounding ovals with words that contain that word root.
3. Write the meaning below each word.

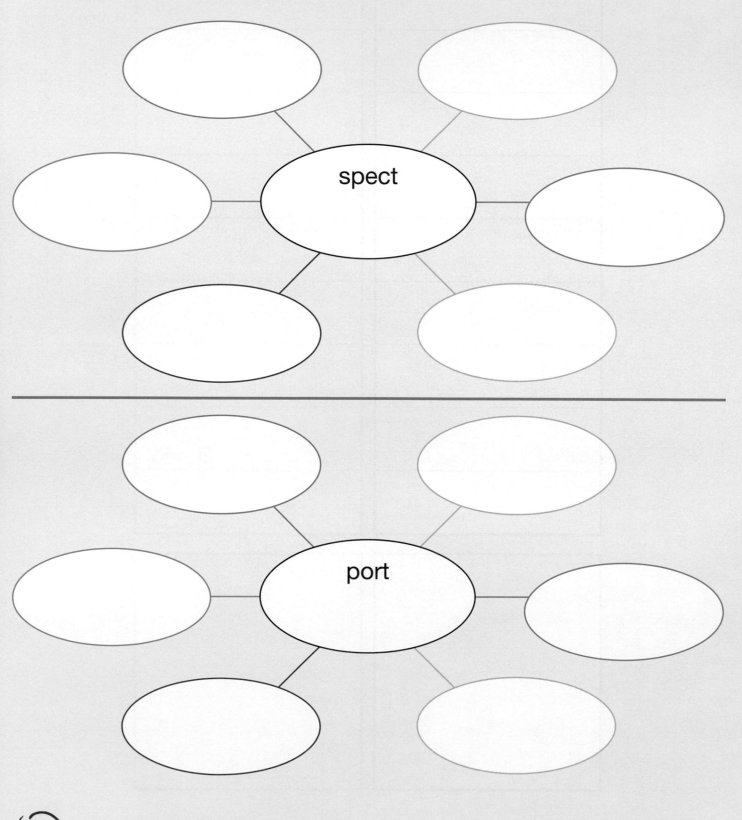

Sort 18: Latin Word Roots spect, port

audible	contradict	auditorium
unpredictable	auditory	verdict
audience	audiotape	dictionary
predict	audition	dictator
audit	diction	audiovisual

dic	aud
dictate	**audio**

1. Write the meaning of each word root next to the headers.
2. Read each word and circle the word root or roots it contains.
3. Write a definition for each word.

dic: _____   **aud:** _____

1. diction _____

2. verdict _____

3. auditory _____

4. predict _____

5. audience _____

6. dictator _____

7. audiotape _____

8. contradict _____

9. auditorium _____

10. unpredictable _____

11. audible _____

12. dictionary _____

13. audition _____

14. audit _____

15. dictate _____

Sort 19: Latin Word Roots dic, aud

subtract	contract	remote
erupt	distract	promotion
rupture	traction	demote
abrupt	attraction	promote
disrupt	tractor	emotion
motor	corrupt	interruption
bankrupt	extract	motivate

rupt	tract	mot
interrupt	**attract**	**motion**

1. Write a definition of each word root.
2. Write a word containing that word root and its meaning.
3. Draw a picture to illustrate the word you defined.

rupt: _____

Word: _____

Definition: _____

tract: _____

Word: _____

Definition: _____

mot: _____

Word: _____

Definition: _____

reject	discredit	injection
eject	objection	manuscript
subject	manage	manufacture
credit	maneuver	credible
projectile	rejection	manicure
manipulate	credentials	

ject	man	cred
inject	**manual**	**incredible**

1. Read each sentence.
2. Choose one word from the box that best completes the sentence and write it on the line. (Note: Not all words have to be used and each word can be used only once.)
3. Circle the word root it contains.

reject	eject	manual	maneuver	discredit	manipulate
projectile	objection	manage	credit	rejection	credentials
injection	manuscript	manufacture	credible	subject	inject

1. The factory was built to _____ canned goods.

2. Ally reached up and caught the _____.

3. Rita didn't find Tom's story about killer bugs _____.

4. The doctor hopes a flu _____ will keep the boy healthy.

5. The climber could easily _____ up the mountain.

6. Sam couldn't _____ his store with a broken leg.

7. Maria's _____ to the competition was there wasn't enough time to practice.

8. The pilot had to _____ from the plane when it went out of control.

9. The author spent several years writing the _____ for his novel.

10. My mother asked me to _____ my least favorite paint colors for my room.

11. Together the students worked on the report for their _____.

12. We read the _____ before using the computer.

Sort 21: Latin Word Roots ject, man, cred

Sort 22

inscription	revise	scribe
provide	television	visionary
description	vista	transcribe
supervise	video	subscribe
prescribe	prescription	inscribe
visible	visit	transcript
postscript	subscription	televise
improvise		

vid/vis	scrib/script
vision	**describe**

1. Read each sentence.
2. Choose one word from the pair in parentheses that best completes the sentence and write it on the line.
3. Circle the word root or roots it contains.

1. The _____ on the inside front cover of the book told us to whom it belonged. (subscription/inscription)

2. I will _____ you with equipment for the rock-climbing trip. (provide/visit)

3. Tara picked up her _____ at the pharmacy. (prescription/description)

4. You have to _____ small children very closely. (supervise/televise)

5. I will _____ the writing on the cave wall so we can study it later. (inscribe/transcribe)

6. After Aiden signed the letter, he added a _____ at the bottom. (transcript/postscript)

7. Eduardo painted a picture of a _____ of the lake. (vista/video)

8. The scientist was such a _____ that he spent all day dreaming of new ideas. (visible/visionary)

9. Do you _____ to any magazines about pets? (scribe/subscribe)

10. Katrina's _____ was connected to her stereo and DVD player. (television/vista)

11. The doctor can _____ an antibiotic for the infant's cold. (prescribe/inscribe)

12. Writers and editors worked to _____ the film before the premiere. (revise/televise)

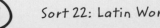

Latin Word Roots jud, leg, flu

legislator	legitimate	judge
flush	prejudge	legislate
influence	fluent	judicial
prejudice	misjudge	legacy
influenza	fluency	privilege

flume
illegal
judgmental
fluctuate
legalize

jud	leg	flu
judgment	**legal**	**fluid**

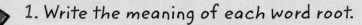

1. Write the meaning of each word root.
2. Read each word and circle the word root it contains.
3. Choose five of the words and write a sentence that uses each word in context.
4. Underline the chosen word in each sentence.

jud: _____   **leg:** _____   **flu:** _____

1. legislate   **5.** influence   **9.** judgmental

2. fluctuate   **6.** prejudge   **10.** legitimate

3. illegal   **7.** influenza   **11.** fluent

4. judicial   **8.** legacy   **12.** legislator

Sentences:

1. _____

   _____

2. _____

   _____

3. _____

   _____

4. _____

   _____

5. _____

   _____

Greek and Latin Elements -crat/-cracy, -arch/-archy

-crat	-cracy	-arch	-archy
autocrat	**autocracy**	**monarch**	**monarchy**
democracy	democrat	oligarchy	technocrat
oligarch	matriarch	plutocrat	anarchist
aristocracy	patriarchy	hierarchy	hierarchical
bureaucracy	bureaucrat	matriarchy	anarchy
aristocrat	technocracy	plutocracy	patriarch

Sort 24: Greek and Latin Elements -crat/-cracy, -arch/-archy

Greek and Latin Elements -crat/-cracy, -arch/-archy

-crat	-cracy	-arch	-archy
autocrat	**autocracy**	**monarch**	**monarchy**

1. Choose two elements (-crat, -cracy, -arch, or -archy) and write one in the center of each web. Write the meaning below each element.
2. Fill the surrounding ovals with words that end with that element.
3. Write the meaning below each word.

Sort 24: Greek and Latin Elements -crat/-cracy, -arch/-archy

inspire	resign	conspire
transpire	insist	assist
insistent	perspire	design
assign	aspiration	insignia
signature	consistent	persist
designate	resistance	cosign

spire	sist	sign
expire	**resist**	**signal**

1. Read each sentence and the word root in parentheses.
2. Complete each sentence by writing a word that contains that word root.
3. Circle the word root in your word.

---

1. The builder will follow the architect's _____. (sign)

2. His greatest _____ was to become an astronaut. (spire)

3. The employee had to _____ her old job to take a better one. (sign)

4. Can you _____ that man crossing the street? (sist)

5. We will _____ together to plan a surprise party. (spire)

6. The teacher will _____ you to a group. (sign)

7. I _____ that you join us for dinner. (sist)

8. Nature may _____ you to write a poem. (spire)

9. The long practice session in the hot gymnasium caused Lorraine to _____. (spire)

10. The cake looked so delicious that we could not _____ it. (sist)

11. The bank requires a _____ on the check. (sign)

12. My baby sister has a _____ nap time. (sist)

13. The coach will _____ two team captains. (sign)

14. The rescue crew will _____ in the storm. (sist)

15. Our free movie pass will _____ soon. (spire)

corporate	peddle	peddler
pedal	incorporate	capitol
pedicure	corps	decapitate
captivity	pedestal	centipede
corporal	captive	captivate
corpse	expedition	captain

cap	ped	corp
capital	**pedestrian**	**corporation**

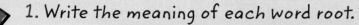

1. Write the meaning of each word root.
2. Read each pair of words and circle the word roots in each word.
3. Choose five pairs of words and write a sentence that uses each word pair. For example, The pedestrian packed a backpack and went on a great expedition. (pedestrian/expedition)

---

cap: _____   **ped:** _____   **corp:** _____

Word Pairs

1. pedicure/peddler

2. corporate/corporal

3. captivate/captive

4. pedal/peddle

5. capital/capitol

6. pedestrian/expedition

7. corps/corpse

8. centipede/pedestal

Sentences:

1. _____

_____

2. _____

_____

3. _____

_____

4. _____

_____

5. _____

_____

divert	insect	landform
format	section	revert
convert	bisect	invert
inform	conversion	formal
conform	advertise	reform
sector	formulate	reverse
universe	uniform	intersect

sect	vert/vers	form
dissect	**version**	**formula**

1. Read each sentence.
2. Choose one word from the box that best completes the sentence and write it on the line. (Note: Not all words have to be used and each word can be used only once.)
3. Circle the word root it contains.

divert	section	inform	intersect	formal	sector
conform	advertise	bisect	convert	invert	conversion
formulate	reform	version	revert	insect	uniform

1. The hallways in the school _____ near the lobby.

2. Workers dug a ditch to _____ water from the stream.

3. Maya will _____ her new store in the newspaper.

4. It took the students quite some time to _____ to the school's new dress code.

5. I am learning how to _____ centimeters to meters.

6. Because we know the star of the play, we got to sit in the front _____ of the theater.

7. Do you prefer the old or new _____ of the game?

8. Manuel took the time to _____ a good answer.

9. Tonya wore her finest clothing for the _____ party.

10. Mark's speech will _____ his classmates on the benefits of recycling.

11. The class gathered facts on the largest _____.

12. In math, we learned to _____ shapes.

onym	gen
synonym	**generator**
antonym	genesis
progenitor	anonymous
patronymic	generic
genre	pseudonym
regenerate	progeny
eponym	genetic
gene	acronym
homonym	hydrogen

onym	gen
synonym	**generator**

1. Write a word containing a word root in each box.
2. Write a sentence and draw a picture to illustrate the meaning of each word.

Word: _____

Sentence: _____

Word: _____

Sentence: _____

Word: _____

Sentence: _____

Word: _____

Sentence: _____

Greek and Latin Word Roots voc, ling, mem, psych

voc	ling	mem	psych
vocal	**linguist**	**memory**	**psychology**
vocalic	linguaphile	memorandum	sociolinguist
vocabulary	psychiatry	memorial	immemorial
remembrance	advocate	invocation	psychopathology
linguini	provocative	psycholinguists	provoke
multilingual	commemorate	invoke	provocation

Sort 29: Greek and Latin Word Roots voc, ling, mem, psych

Greek and Latin Word Roots voc, ling, mem, psych

voc							
vocal							

ling							
linguist							

mem							
memory							

psych							
psychology							

1. Write the meaning of each word root.
2. Read each word and circle the word root it contains.
3. Choose five of the words and write a sentence that uses each word in context.
4. Underline the chosen word in each sentence.

voc: _____ **ling:** _____ **mem:** _____ **psych:** _____

1. provocation

2. linguini

3. commemorate

4. psychiatry

5. memorial

6. linguaphile

7. advocate

8. vocabulary

9. provocative

10. remembrance

11. memorandum

12. sociolinguist

Sentences:

1. _____

_____

2. _____

_____

3. _____

_____

4. _____

_____

5. _____

_____

 Sort 29: Greek and Latin Word Roots voc, ling, mem, psych

intra-	inter-	intro-
intramural	**intermural**	**introvert**
intravenous	intranational	intragalactic
international	introversion	intracellular
introspection	intrapersonal	intercept
intrastate	interpersonal	Internet
interregnum		

intra-	inter-	intro-
intramural	**intermural**	**introvert**

1. Write the definition of each prefix.
2. Write a word containing that prefix and its meaning.
3. Draw a picture to illustrate the word you defined.

intra-: _____

Word: _____

Definition: _____

inter-: _____

Word: _____

Definition: _____

intro-: _____

Word: _____

Definition: _____

 Sort 30: Prefixes intra-, inter-, intro-

ceiv/cep	tain/ten	nounce/nunc
deceive	**retain**	**pronounce**
deception	retention	pronunciation
detain	perception	preconception
preconceive	perceive	attention
detention	attain	sustenance
renounce	denounce	renunciation
denunciation	abstain	sustain
abstention		

ceiv/cep	tain/ten	nounce/nunc
deceive	**retain**	**pronounce**

1. Choose two spelling changes (ceiv/cep, tain/ten, or nounce/nunc), and write one in the center of each web.
2. Fill the surrounding ovals with pairs of words that use the spelling change. For example, retain/retention.

Adding Suffixes -ent/-ence, -ant/-ance #1

-ent	-ence	-ant	-ance
confident	**confidence**	**brilliant**	**brilliance**
dependent	abundant	resident	fragrant
dependence	abundance	residence	fragrance
different	dominant	obedience	excellence
difference	dominance	obedient	patient
prominent	prominence	excellent	patience

Adding Suffixes -ent/-ence, -ant/-ance #1

-ent	-ence	-ant	-ance
confident	**confidence**	**brilliant**	**brilliance**

1. Write the definition of each suffix.
2. Write a word containing that suffix and its meaning.
3. Draw a picture to illustrate the word you defined.

-ent: _____

Word: _____

Definition: _____

-ence: _____

Word: _____

Definition: _____

-ant: _____

Word: _____

Definition: _____

-ance: _____

Word: _____

Definition: _____

Sort 32: Adding Suffixes -ent/-ence, -ant/-ance #1

-ent	-ence	-ant	-ance
imminent	imminence	irrelevant	irrelevance
impertinence	incoherent	inherent	adolescence
abundant	abundance	inconvenience	impertinent
adolescent	incoherence	defiant	iridescent
inconvenient	iridescence	defiance	inherence
adherence	adherent		

Sort 33: Adding Suffixes -ent/-ence, -ant/-ance #2   (129)

-ent	-ence	-ant	-ance
imminent	**imminence**	**irrelevant**	**irrelevance**